Disney

Phineas and Ferb

365 DAYS OF SUMMER!

Answers are on pages 95 & 96.

Based on the series created by Dan Povenmire & Jeff "Swampy" Marsh

Contributing Writer: Kathryn Knight

Copyright © 2011 Disney Enterprises, Inc. All rights reserved.
Published by Dalmatian Press, LLC, in conjunction with
Disney Enterprises, Inc.
www.disneychannel.com
Printed in the U.S.A.

CE14330 Disney Phineas and Freb Big Fun Book to Color

PHINEAS'S CONNECT-A-DOT

Player #1 draws a line to connect two dots. (You can draw up and down, or across, but not diagonally.) Then Player #2 connects two dots. When a player connects two dots and completes a square, he puts his initial inside the square and takes another turn. When all the dots are connected, the game is over. Each initialed square is one point. Squares with sunglasses in them are worth two points. The player with the most points wins!

Player #1: _____ SCORE: _____

Player #2: _____ SCORE: _____

PLAY AGAIN!

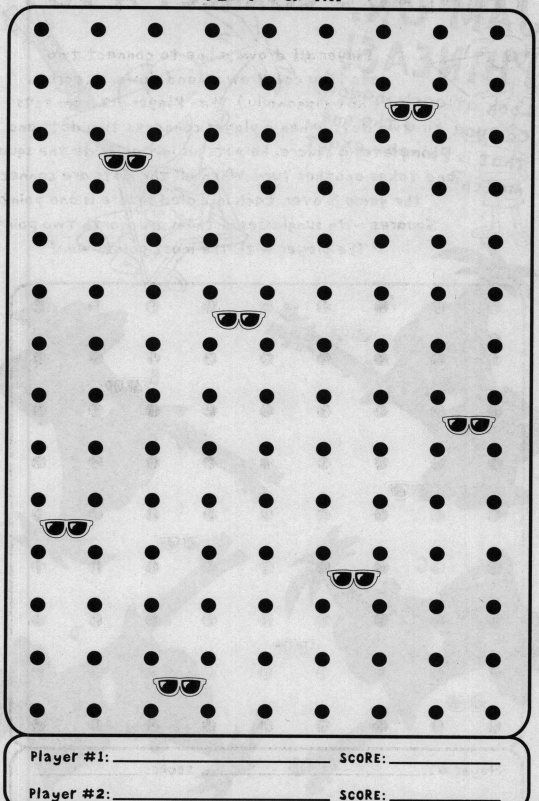

Player #1: _____ **SCORE:** _____

Player #2: _____ **SCORE:** _____

JAM ON, PHINEAS!

Look at each shadow. Can you find the one that is Phineas' exact match?

A

B

C

D

(Answer on page 95)

4

USE THE GRID TO DRAW FERB.

PERRY THE PLATYPUS

Phineas and Ferb have an unusual pet named Perry. He's a platypus. He doesn't do much. (That's what Phineas and Ferb think!)

ARE THESE STATEMENTS ABOUT A PLATYPUS TRUE OR FALSE?

	True	False
1. Lives a semi-aquatic life.	☐	☐
2. Breathes air.	☐	☐
3. Likes to dress up in a ball gown.	☐	☐
4. Has a spur on the hind ankle that delivers a venomous jab.	☐	☐
5. Hatches from an egg.	☐	☐
6. Has a rubbery duckbill snout.	☐	☐
7. Is native to South Africa.	☐	☐
8. Has a thick tail like a beaver.	☐	☐
9. Has webbed, clawed feet like an otter.	☐	☐
10. Enjoys playing mah-jong.	☐	☐
11. Prefers to stay hidden away in a burrow.	☐	☐
12. Emits low growls.	☐	☐

(Answers on page 95)

PHINEAS AND FERB ARE USING A TREASURE MAP TO FIND BADBEARD'S BOOTY ON SPLEEN ISLAND.

Help them get through this tricky maze!

START

FINISH

(Answer on page 95)

AVAST, ME HEARTIES!

The boys have unearthed some booty,
a treasure chest full of fake... what?
To find out, recreate the scene by
drawing the images in each square onto
each corresponding square in the grid.

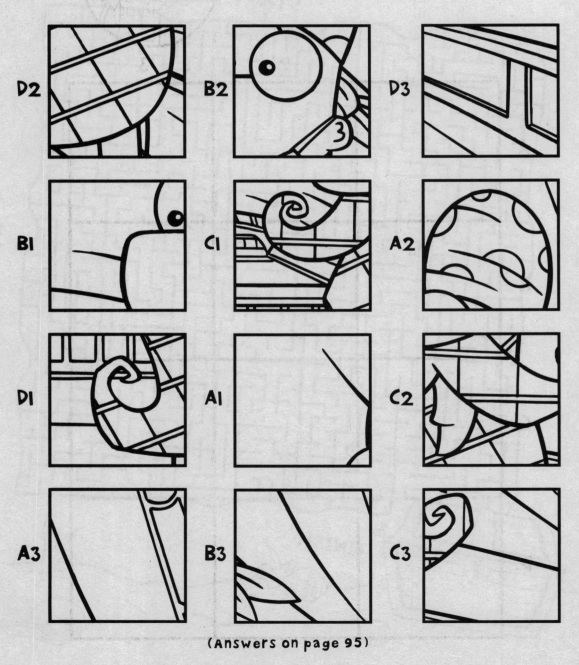

(Answers on page 95)

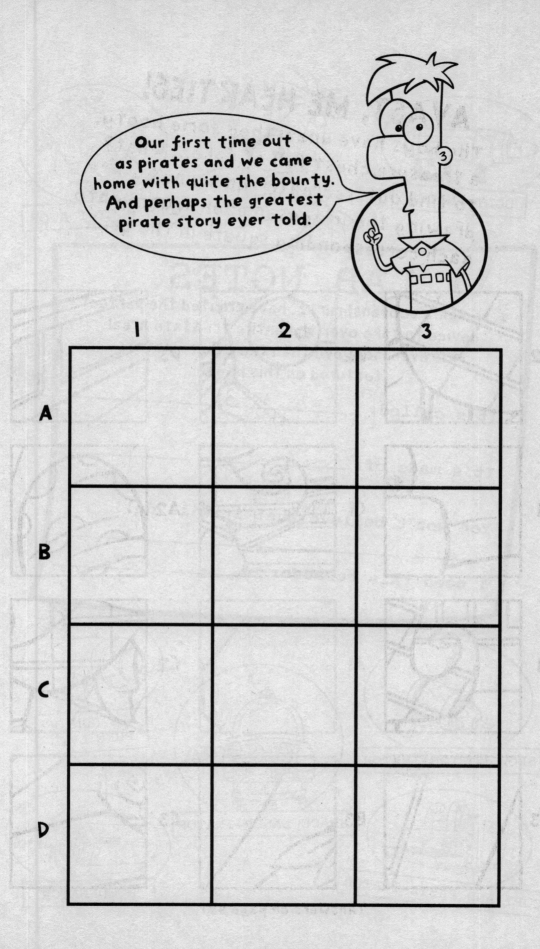

9

UGLY-INATOR

DESTRUCT-INATOR

LAB NOTES

I, Dr. Heinz Doofenshmirtz, have created the perfect device to take over the entire Tri-State Area! It is even more evil than the other -inators featured on this page!

It's called: _____

It's made of: _____

You won't believe what it will do! _____

_____

I need this because: _____

SLOW MOTION-INATOR

SPACE LASER-INATOR

RAY GUN OF PURE EVIL

COPY AND PASTE-INATOR

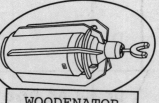

WOODENATOR

Draw Dr. Doofenshmirtz's latest evil invention!

THIS LOOKS LIKE FUN!

Fill in the chart using each letter in Baljeet's name.

	A food	Name of a country	A boy's name
B			
A			
L			
J			
E			
E		Ethiopia	
T			

WORD FIND

Look up, down, across, backward, and diagonally for these words:

FLASH BOLT CHARGED
ROBOTIC EVIL BACKWARD
TIME TRAVEL INATOR

C	P	D	M	O	E		T
M	D	E	S	N	L		I
R	R	G	W	I	I		M
O	A	R	B	N	V		E
B	W	A	I	A	E		T
O	K	H	V	T	L		R
T	C	C	P	O	S		A
I	A	W	B	R	P		V
C	B	J	O	A	Z		E
N	H	S	A	L	F		L

(Answers on page 95)

CANDACE... ALWAYS IN CONTROL.

Look at each shadow. Can you find the one that is Candace's exact match?

(Answer on page 95)

Phineas and Ferb get into and out of jams—and they sure know *how* to jam!

Write your own rockin' song lyrics!

Is this song about me?

Rock on!

DR. HEINZ DOOFENSHMIRTZ

The evil doctor thinks he has fooled you by writing his proclamation in code! But you can decipher it!

KEY

X = L		◉ = D	
⚡ = O	✸ = U	◆ = V	
★ = N	◍ = S	◗ = T	
O = E	✳ = R	◎ = I	

(Answer on page 95)

16

Where's Perry?

Perry the Platypus is
part mindless domestic pet...

How many words with **4** or more letters
can you make using the letters in:

PERRY THE PLATYPUS

...and part secret agent—trying to
save the Tri-State Area from the
very evil Dr. Heinz Doofenshmirtz!

(Answers on page 95)

LOOK AROUND!

1 Look around the room and find something of each color noted in these boxes. Write them down!

2 Then, look around to see if you can spot items that begin with the letters in the boxes and write those down, too!

BLUE	RED	GREEN
____	____	____
ORANGE	PINK	YELLOW
____	____	____
BLACK	PURPLE	GRAY
____	____	____

S	N	P
___	___	___
A	K	J
___	___	___
G	F	R
___	___	___

MY ROBOT

Summer doesn't last forever and the boys have too many plans for just the two of them, so they've made Phinedroids and Ferbots!

What would a robotic **YOU** look like?

I named my amazing robot:

USE THE GRID TO DRAW AGENT P.

GOOD GRADES ARE A JOY!

Look at each shadow.
Can you find the one that
is Baljeet's exact match?

(Answer on page 95)

Danville Trivia

Across

1. He often fears Buford.
5. Candace's mom's first name
6. He can play the concertina.
9. Phineas manages to _____ the Swamp Oil 500.
12. Ferb's dad's first name
14. Ferb's last name
15. Ferb is a man of _____ .
16. Ferbots help make a microscopic _____ .

Down

1. Candace always wants to _____ her brothers.
2. Name of a band: _____ Händel
3. Dr. Doofenshmirtz covers the Eastern Seaboard with _____ foil.
4. The boys search for the treasure of Bad_____ .
7. Phineas' last name
Dr. Doofenshmirtz's brother's name
has a crush on Phineas.
lle is in the _____- _____ Area.
's dad's first name

(Answers on page 95)

FERB'S NOGGIN NUDGER

Fill in the numbers 1 to 9 so that each straight line of three numbers totals 18.

2

6

4   1

(Answers on page 95)

Help Buford
and Baljeet
each find his
own way to
the finish line.

Start

Start

Finish

(Answers on page 95)

PHINEAS AND FERB
HAVE JUST BUILT A TOTALLY AWESOME TREEHOUSE!

Look at the pictures of both treehouses.
Can you find all the differences?
Circle them in the treehouse on page 27.

Hint: There are at least 10.

(Answers on page 96)

BEHOLD, PERRY THE PLATYPUS . . . THE SHRINKSPHERIA!

How many words can you make using the letters in:

SHRINKSPHERIA

_____

_____

_____

_____

_____

_____

_____

_____

_____

_____

_____

_____

(Answers on page 96)

CANDACE'S CONNECT-A-DOT

Player #1 draws a line to connect two dots. (You can draw up and down, or across, but not diagonally.) Then Player #2 connects two dots. When a player connects two dots and completes a square, he or she should put their initial inside the square and take another turn. When all the dots are connected, the game is over. Each initialed square is one point. Squares with a cell phone in them are worth two points. The player with the most points wins!

Player #1: _____ SCORE: _____

Player #2: _____ SCORE: _____

PLAY AGAIN!

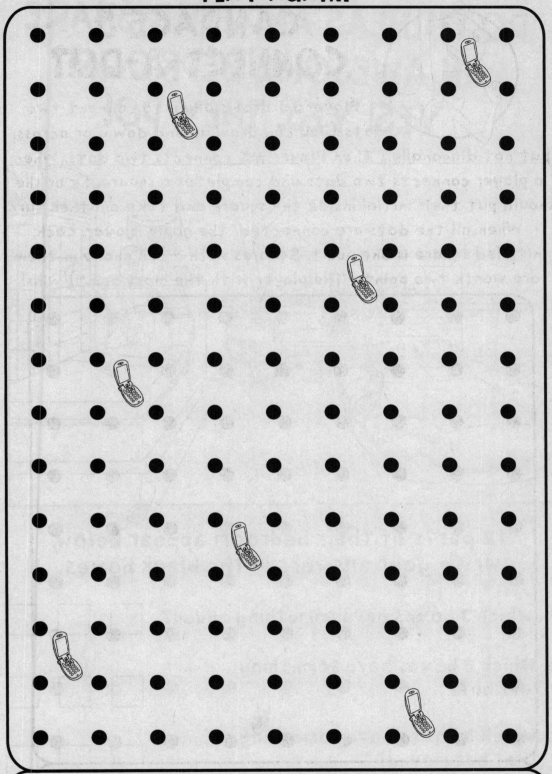

Player #1: _____ SCORE: _____

Player #2: _____ SCORE: _____

DO PHINEAS AND FERB SHARE AN AWESOME BEDROOM? YES! YES, THEY DO!

12 parts of their bedroom appear below.
Write your answers in the blank boxes.

A. Which 3 boxes have something added?

B. Which 3 boxes have something
   left out?

C. Which 3 boxes have something
   that has moved?

D. Which 3 boxes are exactly the same?

(Answers on page 96)

SECRET CODE

Dr. Doofenshmirtz is nowhere to be found! Agent P's superior officer, Major Monogram, gave Agent P two possible reasons for his mysterious disappearance—but they're in code! What do they say?

REASON 1

H I S   I N A T O R
8 9 19   9 14 1 20 15 18

T R A N S P O R T E D
20 18 1 14 19 16 15 18 20 5 4

H I M   T O   A N   A N G R Y
8 9 13   20 15   1 14   1 14 7 18 25

C O R N   L A N D.
3 15 18 14   12 1 14 4

REASON 2

,

H E   S   H I D I N G   O N
8 5   19   8 9 4 9 14 7   15 14

A N   I S L A N D   W I T H
1 14   9 19 12 1 14 4   23 9 20 8

A   G I A N T   D   O N   I T.
1   7 9 1 14 20   4   15 14   9 20

(Answers on page 96)

FINDING A MUMMY

Help Phineas and Ferb find their way to the mummy!

start

Finish

(Answer on page 96)

SUMMER ROCKS!

Fill in the chart using each letter in the word **ROCKS**.

	Name of a city	A food	A cool animal to have as a pet
R			
O			
C			
K		Ketchup	
S			

(Answers on page 96)

USE THE GRID TO DRAW JEREMY.

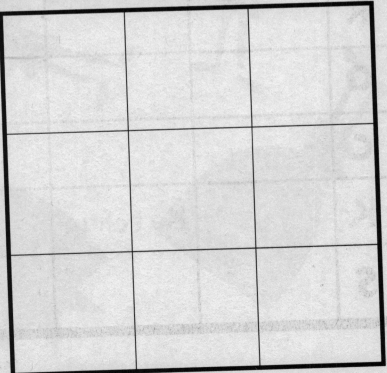

WHATCHA DOIN'?

Look at each shadow. Can you find the one that is Isabella's exact match?

A

B

C

D

(Answer on page 96)

Hey, Buford and Baljeet!
Can you unscramble these letters to spell the names of unusual pets?

No, but I can scramble eggs.

Good one, Buford.

MIXED-UP PETS

KUSNK

_ _ _ _ _

ANAIGU

_ _ _ _ _ _

FREETR

_ _ _ _ _ _

MALLA

_ _ _ _ _

DIPSER

_ _ _ _ _ _

ROONCCA

_ _ _ _ _ _ _

SUPYATPL

_ _ _ _ _ _ _ _

(Answers on page 96)

NAME YOUR NEMESIS!

Grab a nemesis (or a good friend)
and challenge him to some games of
TIC-TAC-TOE.

X name: _____ SCORE: _____

O name: _____ SCORE: _____

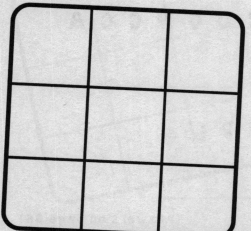

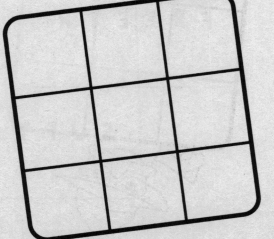

WORD FIND

Can you find the words in the puzzle that describe moves Agent P might make to free himself from the very evil Dr. Doofenshmirtz?

LUNGE JUMP LEAP JAB
BAM SLAP SLAM BOP
STRIKE CHOP PIN HIT

```
S  O  L  J  T  B  P
Y  L  E  U  A  I  O
S  L  A  M  N  B  H
B  O  P  P  A  G  C
D  S  T  R  I  K  E
```

(Answers on page 96)

USE THE GRID TO DRAW
DR. HEINZ DOOFENSHMIRTZ.

WHO'S WHO?

Figure out **WHO** from each character **CLUE** to fill in the crossword puzzle.

Across

1. He lives in Lake Nose.

4. Candace has a crush on him.

6. Carl assists this Major.

8. He often says, "Yes. Yes, I am."

10. This is the name of Isabella's pet chihuahua.

11. He's a man of action.

Down

2. This is the name of Jeremy's little sister.

3. Dr. Doofenshmirtz's first name (hint on p.43)

5. This is the name of Dr. Doofenshmirtz's daughter.

6. This is a cute alien from outer space.

7. This is the Flynn-Fletcher's mindless pet.

9. This is the name of Buford's pet goldfish.

(Answers on page 96)

FERB'S NOGGIN NUDGER

How many total triangles can you find in this picture?

Your answer

Hint: there are more than 12!

(Answer on page 96)

Phineas and Ferb have fixed up their mom's car to race in the Swamp Oil 500! Can you lead them to the finish line?

START

42%

You two are so busted!

FINISH

(Answers on page 96)

Draw lines to match my evil inventions with their names.

SPACE LASER-INATOR

UGLY-INATOR

RAY GUN OF PURE EVIL

SLOW MOTION-INATOR

(Answers on page 96)

WOODENATOR

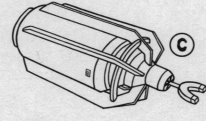

SHRINKSPHERIA

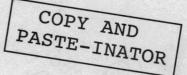

COPY AND
PASTE-INATOR

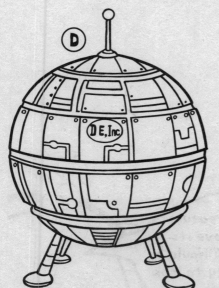

DE,Inc

DESTRUCT-INATOR

(Answers on page 96)

Of all the lakes in the world to visit, the Flynn-Fletcher family picked the Nose! Phineas and Ferb meet Nosey, the Lake Nose Monster. Draw their new friend.

Well, if such a creature did exist, I believe its habitat and safety would be all our responsibility to look after and protect.

Ferb Fletcher —stepbrother and mechanic extraordinaire—has designed a time machine.

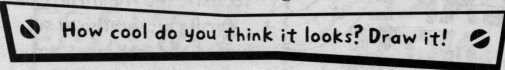

How cool do you think it looks? Draw it!

Riddle

What dog can tell time?

(Answer on page 96)

MIRROR IMAGE

A few of Phineas and Ferb's robots are defective. However, one pair truly reflects the boys. Find the pair that is the exact mirror image of

(Answer on page 96)

Monster MOMENT

What would Ferb have to say about your monster?

Phineas and Ferb have discovered something that doesn't exist—and they brought it home to show Candace.

What do you think it looks like? Draw it here!

HOME PAGE, SWEET HOME PAGE

Phineas and Ferb have developed a new website—and it's driving their sister insane!

What's the home page look like?
Be sure to include fun link buttons!

The first website was nxoc01.cern.ch, created in late 1990.

AGENT P:

Saving the world from maniacal evil one day at a time.

Draw a cool hoverjet for Agent P.

When Perry has a day off, he sometimes watches romantic soaps and eats potato chips. But when Major Monogram gives him an assignment, he goes into action!

Who first invented skateboards? Hard to say! But some say they were invented by bored eight- and nine-year-olds in Los Angeles in the early 1950s. They took the halves of their worn-out roller skates and nailed them to boards—and the rest is history, dude!

It's summer vacation! So, what do you wanna do today?

Help Phineas design the coolest skateboard Danville has ever seen.

Phineas, Ferb, Isabella and Baljeet need your help. Finish designing the most amazing sand castle ever!

WANNA WRITE ZANY TALES™?

ZANY TALES is a fun word game. You can play alone or with friends.

on the next page, you will find blanks with the types of words needed to complete the story. Fill these in—but don't look at the story on the bottom page! When you're done, read the story, inserting the words written on the top page. How zany is your story?

EXAMPLE

ZANY TALE #1

Friend #1 name	1. _____
Musical instrument	2. _____
Friend #2 name	3. _____
Animal	4. _____
Friend #3 name	5. _____
Article of clothing	6. _____

EXAMPLE

BADBEARD'S TREASURE

"Toot-toot!" Phineas and Ferb woke up at camp to a strange sound. "Must be ___①___ playing a(n) ___②___," Phineas said. "Sounds like ___③___ strangling a(n) ___④___ !" They left their tent and noticed that ___⑤___'s ___⑥___ was waving from the flagpole.

Here are some types of words you might use.

Object: A thing. Example: box, guitar, toy, hammer

Object (plural): Make your word plural.
   Example: boxes, bookcases

Action verb (-ing): An action word ending in "ing."
   Example: leaping, singing, throwing

Adjective: A word that describes a person or object.
   Example: awesome, silly, smelly

Adjective (Emotion): A word that describes how someone feels.
   Example: gloomy, joyful, grumpy

Adjective (-est): A description word ending in "est"
   Example: silliest, best, weirdest

Adverb (-ly): How something is done.
   Example: amazingly, slowly, grumpily

Vehicle: Example: car, bike, rocket, scooter, rowboat

Building: Example: library, school, castle, science lab

Shape: Example: triangle, round, oval, square

Exclamation: Example: Wow! That's Awesome! Rats!

ZANY TALE #1

Odd object	1.	_____
Long object (plural)	2.	_____
Wild animal	3.	_____
An appliance	4.	_____
Something sticky	5.	_____
A tool	6.	_____
Adjective (-est)	7.	_____
Adjective	8.	_____
Your street	9.	_____
Reptile (plural)	10.	_____
Something disgusting	11.	_____
Famous landmark	12.	_____
Your school	13.	_____
Friend's name	14.	_____
A city	15.	_____
A planet	16.	_____
Your name	17.	_____

ROLLERCOASTER RIDE

Phineas and Ferb were lugging all sorts of things into the backyard. They had a(n) ___(1)___ , a bunch of ___(2)___ , and even a caged ___(3)___ . They grabbed some tools and began building.

"We're going to need a(n) ___(4)___ and some more ___(5)___ ," said Phineas.

Just then, Isabella walked up to them.

"Whatcha doin'?" she asked.

"Building a rollercoaster," said Phineas.

Ferb just waved with his ___(6)___ .

When they were done, the boys invited their friends to ride the " ___(7)___ coaster ever." The coaster was ___(8)___ ! It climbed and looped, and plunged! When they zoomed down a steep hill, just above ___(9)___ , a bunch of rubber ___(10)___ fell on them! Then they landed in a vat of ___(11)___ !

Next, the coaster left its tracks! It sailed past ___(12)___ , and then past ___(13)___ ! They bounced off of ___(14)___ and were flung all the way to ___(15)___ . They flew around ___(16)___ before heading back to Earth. Then they landed in a tree in ___(17)___ 's backyard. What a wild ride!

"We should have charged more," said Phineas.

ZANY TALE #2

Action verb (-ing)	1. _____
Kind of dinosaur	2. _____
Large animal	3. _____
A liquid	4. _____
High number	5. _____
An odd name	6. _____
A piece of furniture	7. _____
An appliance	8. _____
An insect	9. _____
A number	10. _____
A room in a house	11. _____
Action verb (-ing)	12. _____
Action verb (-ing)	13. _____
Type of container (plural)	14. _____
Food item (plural)	15. _____
Body part (plural)	16. _____
Adverb (-ly)	17. _____
Adjective	18. _____

THAT'S ONE ANCIENT DUDE!

Phineas and Ferb were _____①_____ at the Danville Glacier.

They found a frozen _____②_____ and a frozen _____③_____,

but they finally found what they were looking for: a

frozen caveman! The boys chipped him out of the icy

_____④_____, took him home, and defrosted him. He was

remarkably okay for being over _____⑤_____ years old!

The boys named him _____⑥_____. And, wow, was he

hungry! He tried to eat a(n) _____⑦_____ and a _____⑧_____.

    Phineas got a _____⑨_____ sandwich from Candace

(who had _____⑩_____ of them on a plate) and took it

to _____⑥_____. He loved it! While Phineas and Ferb were

busy in the _____⑪_____, the hungry caveman followed

Candace (and her _____⑨_____ sandwiches) to a party.

    At the party, the loud stereo drove _____⑥_____

crazy! He started _____⑫_____ and _____⑬_____! Then he

spied _____⑭_____ of food and he gorged on _____⑮_____.

When he spotted Candace, the caveman hauled her

onto his shoulders. She screamed and waved her _____⑯_____.

    Finally, Phineas and Ferb arrived to get _____⑥_____.

They _____⑰_____ watched their _____⑱_____ and very old

friend walk off toward the glacier. But if you love

something, you let it go.

ZANY TALE #3

Foreign country   1. _Europe_

Adjective   2. _big_

Adjective   3. _little_

Zoo animal   4. _Lion_

Action verb (-ing)   5. _shooting_

Insect (plural)   6. _caterpillars_

A guy friend's name   7. _Randall_

Something very tall   8. _sky scraper_

Action verb (-ing)   9. _running_

Body part (plural)   10. _heads_

An object   11. _bad tree_

A farm animal   12. _sheep_

Something stinky   13. _rotten eggs_

Adjective   14. _jumping_

Animal (plural)   15. _bear_

GOOD KNIGHT CANDACE

The Flynn-Fletchers went to ___(1)___ to visit their grandparents. Their grandpa showed them a ___(2)___ castle where the ___(3)___ Knight had lived. "The ___(3)___ Knight rode off to chase a ___(4)___. He is said to still be searching to this day," said Grandpa Reg.

That gave Phineas an idea. He and Ferb would hold a tournament for knights! They'd have jousting, a ___(5)___ contest, and roasted ___(6)___ to eat!

Candace agreed to play the damsel in distress after seeing one of the jousters—handsome ___(7)___ from next door. Up in a high ___(8)___, she waited to be rescued. When she discovered that she was locked in, she started ___(9)___ and waving her ___(10)___. She broke through the door with a ___(11)___ and tumbled into a ___(3)___ suit of armor.

Candace stumbled out to where Phineas and Ferb were suited up together in a suit of armor.

"Our jousting partner, ___(7)___!" Phineas exclaimed.

Candace was flung from her ___(12)___ up into the ___(8)___ window, then down the stairs, where she landed on her ___(12)___ again. Galloping off, she got splattered with ___(13)___ and was chased by ___(14)___ ___(15)___.

When ___(7)___ showed up, the boys wondered who the other knight had been.

"The ghost of the ___(3)___ Knight!" their grandpa shouted.

ZANY TALE #4

Friend's name	1.	Henry
Adjective	2.	gigantous
Kind of fish (plural)	3.	Sharks
Body part (plural)	4.	rib bones
An object (plural)	5.	water bottles
Action verb (-ing)	6.	talking
Sea creature (plural)	7.	lock-nes-monsters
Your name	8.	Robert
Object you lost once	9.	Legos
Kind of vehicle (plural)	10.	Porsche
Sticky substance	11.	gum
Sea creature	12.	Star fish
Body part	13.	nose
Exclamation	14.	Oh Goodness!
Type of building	15.	hotel
Food item	16.	spaghetti
Kind of bird (plural)	17.	robin

THE LOST CITY OF ATLANTIS

Phineas, Ferb, Candace, and a bunch of their friends, including ___①___ , were at the beach. Some of the gang declared they were off to find the legendary ___②___ city of Atlantis. Dressed up like ___③___ with air tanks and flippers on their ___④___ , the kids swam off into the water. Candace stayed on the beach with her mom to compete in the sandcastle competition.

The kids saw some really cool stuff underwater. They spotted ___⑤___ and a bunch of ___⑥___ ___⑦___ . They even found ___⑧___ 's ___⑨___ ! They also saw some sunken ___⑩___ with ___⑪___ all over them. ___①___ tried to take pictures, but a(n) ___⑫___ grabbed his camera!

Phineas found a door with old writing on it. Buford used his ___⑬___ to punch through the door. And there before them was Atlantis!

"___⑭___ !" Phineas exclaimed. "Let's bring it up to the surface for everyone to see!"

Back on the beach, Candace kept building her sandcastle. First it looked like a ___⑮___ , then like a(n) ___⑯___ . Just as Jeremy walked over to judge her creation, the Lost City of Atlantis rose near the beach, lifted by four ___⑰___ .

"First place to Candace!" declared Jeremy.

ZANY TALE #5

Article of clothing   1. _____

Sea creature   2. _____

A liquid   3. _____

Action verb (-ing)   4. _____

Something stinky (plural) 5. _____

Sharp object (plural)   6. _____

Insect (plural)   7. _____

Your name   8. _____

Friend's name (girl)   9. _____

Friend's name (boy)   10. _____

Foreign country   11. _____

Soft object (plural)   12. _____

Kind of vehicle   13. _____

Body part   14. _____

Action verb (-ing)   15. _____

Wild animal   16. _____

A number   17. _____

A spice or flavoring   18. _____

ALL PATCHED UP!

Candace is just dying to go to the Paisley Sideburns Brothers concert—but her only chance to get a ticket is to attend the Fireside Girl Jamboree. To become a Fireside Girl, she must earn 50 patches in one day! Candace asks Phineas and Ferb to help her complete the following tasks:

- Sew the _____①_____ for her uniform.
- Wrestle a _____②_____ in a tub of _____③_____.
- Win a _____④_____ contest.
- Eat _____⑤_____ —with no ketchup!
- Juggle _____⑥_____ .
- Collect lots of _____⑦_____ .
- Discover something that doesn't exist— (such as _____⑧_____ doing homework).
- Carve _____⑨_____ and _____⑩_____ names into a totem pole.
- Swim all the way to _____⑪_____ .
- Build a fire using only _____⑫_____ .
- Stop a _____⑬_____ from hitting pedestrians.
- Use only her _____⑭_____ to cook a meal.
- Tend to a _____⑮_____ child.
- Give a _____⑯_____ a shower.
- Deliver _____⑰_____ cases of _____⑱_____ cupcakes.

And she did it! Congratulations, Candace!

ZANY TALE #6

Famous landmark	1.	Statue of Liberty
A liquid	2.	Root Beer
Action verb (-ing)	3.	Jumping
An appliance (plural)	4.	Refrigerators
Zoo animal	5.	Parrot
Farm animal	6.	Cow
Your name	7.	Robert
Action verb (-ing)	8.	Running
Sea creature (plural)	9.	Sharks
A kind of building	10.	Sky Scraper
Type of container	11.	Water Bottle
Exclamation	12.	Yelling!
Cute animal	13.	Lamb
Action verb (-ing)	14.	Watching TV
Body part	15.	Leg

WIZARD OF ODD

When Phineas and Ferb made their house spin to spray-wash it faster (naturally), Candace became dizzy and woke up in a(n) ____(1)____ world! All around her were little ____(2)____ people who all looked like ____(3)____. These ____(3)____ —kins told her she had squished ____(4)____, the evil witch. ____(5)____, the good witch, came ____(6)____ over inside a giant ____(7)____. She gave Candace some red ____(8)____ and sent her down the Yellow Sidewalk to meet the Wizard.

On the way, Candace met ____(9)____, a nerd-crow, who wished to be cool. Together, they skipped ____(10)____ down the path. Phineas and Ferb showed up and suggested they ride ____(11)____ through a wonderland of ____(12)____, but Candace stayed on the Yellow Sidewalk. She met ____(13)____, a talking tree, and ____(14)____, a half-____(15)____, half-____(16)____! They were all captured by Doofenshmirtz, the evil warlock. Candace doused him with ____(17)____ and escaped, finally getting to the Wizard (who was actually ____(18)____), who granted their wishes.

When Candace awoke from her odd dream, she decided that the most fun could be found in your own backyard!

ZANY TALE #8

Adjective   1. _____

Adjective (-est)   2. _____

Type of building   3. _____

Something scary (plural)   4. _____

Sea creature (plural)   5. _____

Name of a monster   6. _____

An object   7. _____

Action verb (-ing)   8. _____

Insect (plural)   9. _____

A friend's name   10. _____

Body part (plural)   11. _____

A color   12. _____

A large number   13. _____

Something stinky   14. _____

Farm animal (plural)   15. _____

Your name   16. _____

Body part (plural)   17. _____

Article of clothing (plural)   18. _____

GET YOUR SCARE ON!

Isabella walked up to Phineas and Ferb. "Whatcha do-hiccup!" she said.

"_____(1)_____ hiccups ya got there," said Phineas. "We'll scare them out of you! We'll build the _____(2)_____ haunted _____(3)_____ ever! With zombies! And _____(4)_____! And _____(5)_____!"

Candace saw her brothers outside. Phineas was carrying a _____(6)_____ head in a jar. Ferb was sharpening a big _____(7)_____. "What are they up to?" she wondered.

The _____(8)_____ _____(9)_____ at the haunted _____(3)_____ scared Isabella! A huge _____(10)_____-like monster had glowing, red _____(11)_____, a _____(12)_____ tongue, and _____(13)_____ teeth! One room had piles of _____(14)_____ guarded by howling _____(15)_____!

"Behold the face of evil!" called a deep voice. It was Buford, dressed up as _____(16)_____!

"Hiccup!" responded Isabella.

When Candace was in the haunted _____(3)_____, a giant floating baby head made her scream and wave her _____(17)_____! "Phineas is so busted!" she fumed.

However, a jet carried the whole _____(3)_____ off— with Phineas inside! He fell out, but luckily the Fireside Girls quickly made a net out of _____(18)_____ and saved him!

"That was scary!" said Isabella—with no hiccups!

ZANY TALE #9

Exclamation   1. _____

Adjecive   2. _____

Name of a friend   3. _____

An object   4. _____

A kind of room   5. _____

An appliance   6. _____

A color   7. _____

An object (plural)   8. _____

Action verb (-ing)   9. _____

Action verb (-ing)   10. _____

A job title (plural)   11. _____

Slimy object (plural)   12. _____

A liquid   13. _____

Adverb (-ly)   14. _____

A color   15. _____

A food   16. _____

TREE HOUSE FIGHT

Phineas and Ferb showed Isabella their remodeled tree house. "___(1)___!" exclaimed Isabella. Then they noticed Candace's old tree house. "Kinda ___(2)___," said Isabella. So the trio decided to remodel it.

Phineas told Candace and her friend ___(3)___ to check out her new tree house. They used a ___(4)___ to swing up the tree. Wow! Her tree house had a ___(5)___ with a ___(6)___! It had ___(7)___ ___(8)___! It was so fab!

"Push the 'THF' button!" Phineas called out. What could that be? ___(3)___ pushed the button. TREE HOUSE FIGHT!

The two trees uprooted and became robot-like warriors, with the kids in each tree house manning the controls! The trees began ___(9)___ and ___(10)___. "Bring it on!" yelled ___(3)___. Phineas and Ferb, dressed as ___(11)___, threw ___(12)___ at the girls. BAP! The girls fired back with ___(13)___-filled balloons. SPLAT!

Mrs. Flynn-Fletcher called to say she'd be home soon, so the kids and trees ___(14)___ headed for the backyard. "Last one home is a big ol' ___(15)___ pickled ___(16)___!" called Phineas.

ZANY TALE #10

Friend #1 name	1. _____
Musical instrument	2. _____
Friend #2 name	3. _____
Animal	4. _____
Friend #3 name	5. _____
Article of clothing	6. _____
Number	7. _____
Adjective	8. _____
A U.S. State	9. _____
Article of clothing	10. _____
Adjective	11. _____
Body part (plural)	12. _____
Adjective	13. _____
Insect	14. _____
A city	15. _____
Adjective	16. _____
Adjective	17. _____
Object (plural)	18. _____

BADBEARD'S TREASURE

"Toot-toot!" Phineas and Ferb woke up at camp to a strange sound. "Must be ___①___ playing a(n) ___②___ ,"Phineas said. "Sounds like ___③___ strangling a(n) ___④___ !" They left their tent and noticed that ___⑤___'s ___⑥___ was waving from the flagpole.

"Cool!" Phineas shouted.

The boys and their ___⑦___ friends went to Badbeard's Lake, named for captain Badbeard, a(n) ___⑧___ pirate from ___⑨___. "Badbeard hid his treasure on Spleen Island," Phineas and Ferb's grandfather explained. He pulled a map from his ___⑩___ and read: "Whoever dares to open the treasure chest will be cursed with ___⑪___ ___⑫___ forever!"

"Cool!" Phineas cheered.

Ferb helped the kids build a ___⑬___ ship, and they sailed off toward the island. They were chased by a giant ___⑭___ all the way to ___⑮___ Cave! There they found Badbeard's treasure chest! It was full of ___⑯___, ___⑰___, tacky ___⑱___!

ZANY TALE #11

Type of fish	1. _____
Girl's name	2. _____
Type of container	3. _____
Adjective	4. _____
Adjective (emotion)	5. _____
Action verb (-ing)	6. _____
Sea creature (plural)	7. _____
Wild animal (plural)	8. _____
Color	9. _____
Strange animal	10. _____
Reptile (plural)	11. _____
Body part	12. _____
Large number	13. _____
Tall object	14. _____
Action verb (-ing)	15. _____
Sea creature	16. _____
Adjective	17. _____

BACKYARD AQUARIUM

Phineas and Ferb had a new pet—a ___①___ named

___②___ . They watched her swim around in a

___③___ .

"Let's do something special for her," said Phineas.

Ferb agreed. He showed Phineas blueprints for

a backyard aquarium.

" ___④___ idea!" cheered Phineas.

Once they placed ___②___ inside the aquarium,

the boys realized that she might be ___⑤___ and

lonely. So they went ___⑥___ off to the sea to find

some other creatures. They brought back ___⑦___ ,

___⑧___ , and a ___⑨___ ___⑩___ and added them

all to the aquarium. One of the ___⑪___ ate ___②___

and blew her back out through its ___⑫___ .

"Cool trick!" Phineas exclaimed. "Let's have

a trained animal show!"

A crowd gathered to watch as ___⑬___ aquatic

creatures performed amazing feats. Suddenly, a

creature fell from a ___⑭___ into the water and

began ___⑮___ !

"That's no ___⑯___ !" cried Phineas. "That's my

___⑰___ sister, Candace!"

ZANY TALE #12

Large object (plural) 1. Daddy's bottom

Adjective 2. cute

Your name 3. Nicole

Animal 4. snake

Action verb (-ing) 5. jumping

A food 6. mac & cheese

Object 7. Munny

Round object (plural) 8. heads

Something sticky 9. slime

A color 10. Black White

Adjective (emotion) 11. Back hurt

Adjective 12. fast

Wild animal 13. raccoon

A liquid 14. juice

Body part 15. leg

MUMMY MADNESS

Phineas, Ferb, and Candace went to see a movie with their dad: *The Mummy with Two* ___①___ . In the movie, two ___②___ explorers read messages carved in the wall.

"o-wah ta-foo-liss ___③___ ," they read, bringing the mummy back to life to obey all their commands.

"Well, beat me with a(n) ___④___ !" exclaimed one explorer. So the mummy did!

The boys wanted their own mummy! As they went ___⑤___ off to find one, Candace followed. But she knocked over a huge ___⑥___ machine, then stepped into a(n) ___⑦___ while fleeing ___⑧___ rolling after her. She went into a supply closet, only to be covered in ___⑨___ and ___⑩___ toilet paper!

Phineas and Ferb were thrilled to encounter this wrapped creature! Their very own mummy!

"Imagine the ___⑪___ , ___⑫___ soul hidden underneath those bandages," said Phineas.

Ferb roped the mummy and the boys rode it like a bucking ___⑬___ . But a sudden rush of ___⑭___ washed all the paper off—revealing Candace!

"You know, mummies had their brains pulled out through their ___⑮___ ," said Ferb.

"Ah, the lucky ones!" replied Candace.

ZANY TALE #13

Adjective	1.	_____
A food	2.	_____
A liquid	3.	_____
A planet	4.	_____
Tiny creature (plural)	5.	_____
Insect (plural)	6.	_____
Large creature (plural)	7.	_____
Your name	8.	_____
Action verb (-ing)	9.	_____
Action verb (-ing)	10.	_____
Body part (plural)	11.	_____
Action verb (-ing)	12.	_____
Something sticky	13.	_____
A kind of container	14.	_____
Kind of vehicle	15.	_____
Something stinky	16.	_____
Fairytale character	17.	_____
Adjective	18.	_____

BROBOTS

Phineas and Ferb sat under their backyard tree, wondering what ___(1)___ thing they should do that day. Maybe a ___(2)___-based ___(3)___ park! Maybe a tunnel to the center of ___(4)___. Maybe a microscopic zoo with ___(5)___, ___(6)___, and ___(7)___!

"We've got too many plans for just the two of us," said Phineas. "We need more days—or more of us."

So they decided to make robots of themselves! They made Ferbots and Phinedroids. (They even made a robo-___(8)___.) Ferb set the control to dance mode. The robots began ___(9)___ and ___(10)___! Then each robot grabbed a blueprint and tools to begin a project.

When Candace looked in the backyard, her ___(11)___ stuck straight up and she began ___(12)___. "They're brobots!" she shrieked. She set out a can of ___(13)___ to tempt a Ferbot—then captured it in a ___(14)___ and put it by the curb. A ___(15)___ came by and picked up the ___(14)___. Then a truck delivered a ___(14)___ of ___(16)___.

Just as Candace tried to show the brobots to her mom, ___(17)___ flew overhead in a sleigh with giant magnets, lifting the brobots from the yard. But Candace confidently dumped the ___(14)___ to show the Ferbot.

"Very ___(18)___ ___(16)___, Candace," her mom said.

ZANY TALE #14

A liquid   1. _____

A baking ingredient   2. _____

A spice   3. _____

Food item   4. _____

Something slimy   5. _____

Food item (plural)   6. _____

Insect (plural)   7. _____

A vegetable   8. _____

A song title   9. _____

Adjective   10. _____

Your father's name   11. _____

Geometric shape (plural)   12. _____

Sea creature (plural)   13. _____

Insect (plural)   14. _____

Adjective   15. _____

Article of clothing   16. _____

Action verb (-ing)   17. _____

Adjective   18. _____

MOM'S BIRTHDAY

Phineas and Ferb were making plans. It was their mom's birthday! They made her special coffee with ___(1)___, ___(2)___, and a dash of ___(3)___. They went in to her room to surprise her with it just as Candace was bringing her mom ___(4)___ and ___(5)___ for breakfast. Candace got trapped behind the door—breakfast and all!

When their mom came downstairs, the boys presented her with *their* breakfast: toasted ___(6)___, scrambled ___(7)___, and freshly squeezed ___(8)___ juice. They also gave her a big birthday card that played ___(9)___. When she said she'd love a ___(10)___ dress for her birthday, Candace rushed off to ___(11)___'s Fashions and selected a dress with ___(12)___ and little ___(13)___.

Unfortunately, on the way back from the store, a horde of ___(14)___ descended and ate holes in the dress. Candace arrived home to find her brothers giving their mom a ___(15)___ ___(16)___. Candace started ___(17)___ when the ___(14)___ attacked her... but she ended up singing a fab song for her mom, and Mrs. Flynn-Fletcher had a ___(18)___ birthday!

ZANY TALE #15

An animal   1. _____

Friend's name   2. _____

Adjective   3. _____

A food item   4. _____

A board game   5. _____

Electronic device   6. _____

An object   7. _____

Year you were born   8. _____

Your name   9. _____

Exclamation   10. _____

Action verb (-ing)   11. _____

Body part (plural)   12. _____

Kind of vehicle   13. _____

Action verb (-ing)   14. _____

Body part (plural)   15. _____

IT'S ABOUT TIME

Phineas and Ferb were at the Danville Museum. Their dad found a ___①___ skeleton —with a collar that said ___②___. "Didn't we have a pet ___①___ named ___②___?" asked Phineas.

The boys saw ___③___ things in the museum. A petrified ___④___. A caveman version of ___⑤___. An ancient ___⑥___ carved from wood. In one exhibit, the boys saw an unfinished time machine. "I know what we're gonna do today!" Phineas exclaimed.

Phineas and Ferb got right to work on the old machine. The one missing piece (a ___⑦___) showed up just in time. Candace walked over as the boys tested the machine, and they all went back to the year ___⑧___, where a giant ___⑨___-osaurus smashed the machine!

"___⑩___!" yelled Phineas. Candace started ___⑪___ and waving her ___⑫___. Phineas and Ferb followed in a ___⑬___ as the ___⑨___-osaurus chased Candace.

Isabella and the Fireside Girls built a new time machine and rescued the boys and Candace. However, the ___⑨___-osaurus came back with them, chasing Candace again as she went ___⑭___ and waving her ___⑮___ all around the museum.

ZANY TALE #16

Adjective   1. _____

Friend's name   2. _____

Odd object   3. _____

Sea creature   4. _____

Action verb (-ing)   5. _____

Body part (plural)   6. _____

Adjective (-est)   7. _____

Tall object   8. _____

A color   9. _____

Disgusting substance   10. _____

Kind of vehicle (plural)   11. _____

Action verb (-ing)   12. _____

Something slimy   13. _____

Adjective   14. _____

Object (plural)   15. _____

GELATIN—IT'S ALIVE!

Candace was having a gelatin party with her ___①___ friends. Candace's gelatin mold was shaped like ___②___'s head. Stacey's was shaped like a(n) ___③___. Jenny's was shaped like a(n) ___④___.

When Phineas and Ferb came into the room and started ___⑤___ on their gelatins, Candace waved her ___⑥___ and yelled, "Get out! Go make your own gelatin!"

"I know what we're gonna do today!" Phineas cheered.

The boys ran to Isabella's backyard to use her pool as the "largest and ___⑦___ gelatin mold ever." Ferb got up onto a ___⑧___ to pour the ___⑨___ mix into the pool. Baljeet added his favorite flavor, ___⑩___. The Fireside Girls stirred the mix by riding ___⑪___ around in the pool. Once the gelatin had set and become firm, the kids all started ___⑫___ on it, having a great time!

However, the pool of gelatin was hit by the evil Dr. Doofenshmirtz's Turn-Everything-Evil-inator, making it come alive! It looked like a huge mass of ___⑬___! The kids all turned angrily to Baljeet.

"It was the ___⑩___ you added!" they said.

Everything turned out okay, though. After the ___⑭___ monster swallowed Candace, the kids threw ___⑮___ at it, and it finally glubbed away down the pool drain.

ZANY TALE #17

A number   1. _____

A color   2. _____

Geometric shape (plural)   3. _____

Action verb (-ing)   4. _____

Adjective   5. _____

Article of clothing   6. _____

Kind of container   7. _____

Sea creature   8. _____

Sea creature   9. _____

Food item (plural)   10. _____

Kind of building   11. _____

Action verb (-ing)   12. _____

Body part (plural)   13. _____

Animal   14. _____

Insect   15. _____

A color   16. _____

Something gooey   17. _____

SWISS FAMILY PHINEAS

Phineas and Ferb set sail on a ___(1)___-hour tour with their parents, Candace, and Isabella. The sky grew ___(2)___ with ___(3)___, and a storm arose, which sent the boat ___(4)___! The small boat was tossed onto a ___(5)___ deserted island!

Everyone was okay, although Ferb lost his ___(6)___, and Candace ended up with a ___(7)___ on her head, which contained a(n) ___(8)___ and a(n) ___(9)___!

Mr. Fletcher told Candace to find some ___(10)___ to eat. He told the boys to go build a ___(11)___ for shelter. "We might be here for a while," he explained.

This, of course, made Candace start ___(12)___ and waving her ___(13)___. It didn't help matters when a wild ___(14)___ tried to kiss her. The boys offered Candace a ___(15)___ smoothie, but she stormed off.

"Watch out!" warned Phineas as he, Ferb, and Isabella suddenly ran past her. Candace looked and screamed! A ___(16)___ wave pouring from a volcano swept her and everyone else onto the boat. The wave of ___(17)___ pushed the boat all the way home (with Perry the Platypus water-skiing behind them).

what shall we build today?

Now, check out the answers on the next two pages. See you next time!

Answers

Page 4: A

Page 6:
1. T, 2. T, 3. F, 4. T, 5. T, 6. T, 7. F, 8. T,
9. T, 10. F, 11. T, 12. T

Page 7:

Page 8: Fake Beards

Page 12: Possible Answers

	A food	Name of a country	A boy's name
B	Banana	Belize	Ben
A	Apple	Australia	Austin
L	Lettuce	London	Luke
J	Jelly	Japan	Joe
E	Egg	Egypt	Ethan
E	Eggplant	Ethiopia	Evan
T	Tomato	Turkey	Tom

Page 13:

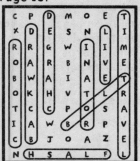

Page 14: C

Page 16:
Evil Doers Unite!

Page 17:
Possible Answers: pray, tray, play, stay, splat,
they, theater, year, plate, rate, super, that,
these, heat, rust, test, sphere

Page 21: D

Page 23:

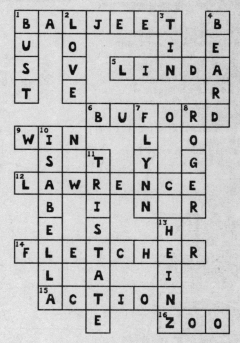

Page 24:

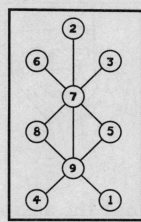

Page 25:

Answers

Page 27:

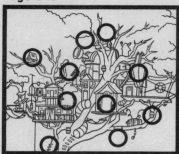

Page 29:
Possible answers: ink, rink, sink, rank, sank, rake, pine, shine, pan, ran, hen, snake, hair, pear

Page 33:
A-1, 6, 9; B-2, 3, 5; C-7, 8, 11; D-4, 10, 12

Page 34:
Reason 1: His inator transported him to an angry corn land.
Reason 2: He's hiding on an island with a giant D on it.

Page 35:

Page 36: Possible Answers

	Name of a city	A food	A cool animal to have as a pet
R	Reno	Rice	Rabbit
O	Orlando	Olive	Ostrich
C	Chicago	Carrot	Cat
K	Kalamazoo	Kale	Kangaroo
S	Seattle	Salad	Snake

Page 38: B

Page 39:
SKUNK, LLAMA, IGUANA, SPIDER, FERRET, RACCOON, PLATYPUS

Page 40: B

Page 42:

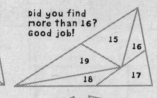

Page 45:

Page 46:
1 (entire triangle)
Did you find more than 16? Good job!
more than 23? Brilliant!
If you found 28, you're as smart as Ferb!

Page 47:

Page 48:
A-Slow Motion-inator
B-Ugly-inator
C-Ray Gun of Pure Evil
D-Space Laser-inator

Page 49:
A-Copy and Paste-inator
B-Destruct-inator
C-Woodenator
D-Shrinkspheria

Page 51: A watch dog

Page 52: C